Children of the
Clearances

CORBIE

Text by David Ross
Illustrated by Tony O'Donnell

© 2001 Waverley Books Ltd

Reprinted 2002

Published by Waverley Books Ltd
New Lanark, Scotland

ISBN 1 902407 18 0

Printed and bound in Slovenia

Children of the
Clearances

THE CLEARANCES

My name is Jessie. I am going to tell you about some of the things that happened in Scotland during a time in our history called the Clearances.

In the Highlands and Islands, many Scottish clansmen and their families were forced to leave their homes during the Clearances. They were living on small farms but the men who owned the land wanted to set up huge sheep farms. They believed the only way to do this was to drive the ordinary people away. And so it was that poor people, like my family, lost not only their belongings and their homes but their whole way of life. Many were forced to leave Scotland forever to seek a new life in the colonies.

Many children suffered as a result of the Clearances, including my own brothers and my sister. I am going to tell you a little about how our lives changed during this time. You can also read in this book about how some other people felt about what was happening. They include a rich and powerful Duke and his Duchess, their factor (the man who looked after their lands) and his son.

When this story begins, I was living with my granny and my younger sister and brothers in Suisinish on the Isle of Skye . . .

THE CHILDREN OF SUISINISH, ISLE OF SKYE

Our granny is a very old lady. My sister, Margaret, my two younger brothers, Murdo and Alexander, and I live with our granny because our mother died a year ago. Our daddy, Alexander Matheson, has gone away to the South, to work at the harvest on the big farms. He has taken our big brother with him. They will come back before the winter, with the money they have earned.

Granny can't walk any more but we all help carry her out to the front of the house when the sun is shining. She likes to sit there and see what is happening. From the house we look down onto the blue waters of Loch Slapin. All around us are small fields in which there are corn and potatoes growing, with cows and sheep on the green hills. Across the loch we can see heather-covered hills and, rising beyond them, the distant peaks of the great Cuillin Mountains. I think we live in the most lovely place in the world – when it isn't raining!

But on this fine, sunny day – what do we hear? The dogs are barking, all along the houses. We can hear people shouting, far off. Something very strange is happening. Little Alexander and I stay with our granny, and Margaret and Murdo climb over the wall and run to see what is going on. Perhaps it is a pedlar come to

8

sell needles and trinkets? But it doesn't sound like a pedlar arriving.

"Is it our daddy coming back?" asks Alexander, who is too young to know that his daddy won't come back until the harvest is over and it is nearly winter.

But when Murdo and Margaret come running back, their faces are pale and scared.

"What's the matter?" I ask them.

They are too breathless to speak properly.

"The men –" gasps Margaret. "Men are coming. They are throwing everything out of the houses! They are putting the people out and nailing up the doors!"

"They are tipping out the meal chests and smashing up the furniture," says Murdo. "Why are they doing it? Who are they?"

Granny throws up her arms in horror.

"It is the Laird's men! Lord MacDonald has sent them, as he threatened he would. He wants to take the land we have always lived on and turn it into a great sheep farm. Alas, that I should live to see the day."

"I won't let them come here," says Murdo, with a fierce face, picking up a stick as if it was a sword.

"But where can we go?" cries Margaret. She looks at me. I am the oldest. But I don't know.

"Let us go inside the house," I say. "Take Granny inside. Surely when they see there is just an old woman and children here, they will leave us alone. They wouldn't put us out."

And that is what we do. Poor old granny is crying and moaning as we stagger through the narrow door with her chair. I push the door shut. It is nearly dark inside our little house and smoky from the peat fire that is still smouldering. Bright light comes in through the narrow window and we all squeeze close, trying to look out and see what is happening.

"They are coming!" cries Margaret, and she catches hold of me in her fright and tries to hide her face in my plaid.

In a minute, there is a heavy hammering on the door.

"Come out!" roars a man's big voice.

We do not move and, with a crash, the door is pushed open and men come bursting into the room.

"What have we got here?" says one. "An old wife and a parcel of bairns. Out with the lot of you. This place is being cleared."

"Leave us alone!" shouts Murdo, and runs at the man, though he only comes up to his waist. The man catches Murdo and pushes him out through the door. In another moment they have picked up Granny's chair and carried her outside again. Crying, we follow, but the men pay no attention to us. Now out through the door come all the things we have – one or two chairs, a milking stool, the spinning wheel, all tossed into a broken heap. It does not take long to empty our poor little house. Then hammer, hammer – strong wooden bars are fixed across the door and windows.

"Where can we go?"

"What can we do?"

The men do not answer. Without looking back at us, they tramp on to the next house.

Mary MacDonald, from the next croft, comes to our wall and looks over.

"They are devils, these men. They chose their time well, with our men away and only the old folk and the women and children to face them. Is the old lady all right?" she calls.

"I think so. I don't know," I answer her. "What is happening? What are you going to do?"

"We will walk to Broadford," she said. "I have cousins there who will take us in for a short time at least, until my husband returns. I would offer to take you too but I have my own three children, and their house is so small."

"My granny cannot walk," I answer. "We can't leave her. We cannot go from here."

"It is a desperate day," said Mary MacDonald. "I will tell them in Broadford and hope that something can be done. But I must go, or it will be night before I get there, with my baby to carry and my two cows to drive through the hills."

All that day we watch the people of Suisinish straggle away from their old homes. They carry heavy burdens and long memories of the land they had believed to be their own. None of them can help us.

Clouds are rising now to hide away the sun and the blue water of Loch Slapin has turned a greeny-grey colour. The men had tipped our bag of oatmeal and our little stock of potatoes out on the grass. Murdo and Margaret gather up the potatoes while I scrape the meal together again, find a dish, mix some of the oatmeal with water and make us a cold and miserable dish of brose. A chilly wind is coming in from the sea. We often look back at our house, locked and barred. It seems so hard to believe such a thing could happen in this land.

While we eat, I am thinking of what we might do, and then I remember the sheepcot on the hillside. It is no house but it has walls and a roof and offers some kind of shelter. I make up my mind.

"We will go to the old sheepcot," I say to the others. And I make them gather up what they can – bits of bedding, some clothes – and carry them up the hill. After two or three trips, we are ready to move granny. But it is one thing to carry her from her bed in the house to the front door, and something else to carry her a long way up a steep hill. We cannot do it – we are just not big and strong enough. Having got the old lady out of her chair, we have to lay her down on the ground.

"You are good children," she says, over and over again, "you do not deserve this to happen to you."

Slowly, slowly, we help her along. Most of the way our poor granny has to crawl, though where the ground

is level, we help her to her feet and she walks a few tottery steps.

It is horrible inside the sheepcot. It is made of rough stones and wind blows through chinks and gaps. Under our feet the ground is slippery and it is dark, smelly and damp. There is no fireplace or chimney hole and we have to light a fire outside. We stay out as long as we can, saying nothing, watching the long slow twilight fall across the hills, wondering what will happen to us.

THE FACTOR'S SON

When I grow up, I'm going to be a farmer. I'll have thousands of sheep. That's what my daddy says. Sheep-farming is the future of the Highlands. My daddy's name is Mr William Gunn and he is an important man. He is the factor to the Duke of Sutherland and we live in a nice house in Golspie, near the Duke's castle. The Duke is often away and my father manages things for him.

I have to work hard at my lessons, so that I can learn to count, and read, and write. A farmer needs to know these things. Some of the children from round here never go to school. I know some of them. They don't talk English but only Gaelic. I know a little bit of Gaelic but I have to be careful when I talk to them. If my daddy hears me talking Gaelic, he gets very angry. He says it is the language of the olden days and people should be forbidden to speak it.

"Everyone should talk the Queen's English," he says. "Gaelic is for savages."

Here in Golspie everyone is very polite to my father and men take their hats off to him in the street. Sometimes they whisper in his ears, telling him things. Some people are very naughty, and at night they will go out and catch fish from the Duke's river, or go down

to the sea and gather shellfish that belong to the Duke. Everything here belongs to the Duke, you see. My father has had to send people away from the village for doing such things. My mother is always upset when this happens.

"These people were hungry," I heard her say to him, once.

"They can go and find their food somewhere else," said my daddy. "Give them any kindness and they'll be back begging for more. A man must do his duty."

A while ago, I was sick and, when I was getting better, my father took me out into the country with him.

"A bit of fresh air will do you good," he said, "we'll put some colour into that peelie-wally face of yours."

I sat proudly in front of him on his big brown horse. About twenty men were riding with him and we followed a path up into the hills. The sun was shining and everyone was talking and laughing. A man looked across at me. "Is he a chip off the old block?" he asked.

"I hope so," said my daddy, ruffling my hair.

We came to a place where there were fields and houses in a green valley. A crowd of women and children were waiting as we came up, and they started crying out and going down on their knees in front of us. My father stopped his horse.

"Get out of the way! If you make any trouble, I will have soldiers come and shoot the lot of you," he shouted, in a fierce voice.

Then he waved his men on. They dismounted from their horses, ran into the houses and began throwing out all the bits of furniture. I saw an old, old man being carried out on his bed. Soon there was smoke rising into the air. My father's men were setting fire to the empty houses. With his arm round me, my father sat on his horse, watching. He gave me an apple to eat.

"What is happening, Daddy?" I asked him. "Why are the men doing this?"

"These people do not understand," he said. "They have to be moved out. You can't just put sheep on the hillside; you need the green valleys too. Men from the South will pay the Duke a good price to breed sheep here. All these people were given fair warning to get out. Just because they have always lived here, they think they can keep on living here for ever."

"But Daddy, they are crying. Where can they go?"

"There are too many of them," he said. "I don't care where they go, as long as they get away from here and off the Duke's land."

"But doesn't the Duke own all the land?"

"You're too young to understand," said my father. "These people don't matter. They are not important. Look at their houses – no better than huts. They can't even speak English. This is the nineteenth century, not the Middle Ages. They must learn to move with the times."

As we rode back to Golspie, I could smell the smoke

on my father's coat. Somewhere along that road I decided that I didn't want to be a sheep farmer any more. But I didn't tell my daddy. I don't think he would understand.

THE DUKE

I am His Grace the Duke of Sutherland. I am the owner of Sutherlandshire and I am a very angry man. You would think the people who live on my estates would have some respect for me. Well, just listen to this. You may know that this year, 1854, Britain and France have just gone to war against Russia. Now, it is one of the fine traditions of the Highlands of Scotland that, when the army needs men, the Highlanders are always first to come forward. Our Highland regiments are the finest there are and, if I may say so, the Sutherland Highlanders are the finest of all.

I called all my tenants to a meeting and came down from my castle to talk to them. I invited the young men to join up to fight the Russians. I offered them a special payment and showed them the gold and the pound notes, right there and then. Would you believe it – not one single man stepped forward. Disgraceful!

Then at last, an old man stood up. He spoke in a low voice, but in the silence, every word was clear. He reminded me of the day when my wife's grandmother, the Countess of Sutherland, had assembled a regiment of nine hundred men in this very place. She could easily have doubled their number. And then he said:

"But in her day, the glens of Sutherland were full of

people. Today, the glens are empty and desolate places. The men of Sutherland have seen their houses torn down, their wives and children forced out, and for what? So that the noble and rich Duke and Duchess of Sutherland could become even richer by replacing them with sheep. And now you find, when you need men, there are none who will answer your call. Perhaps you had better send your sheep to fight for you."

And some of the fellows skulking in the back row called out: "Baa! Baa!"

It was intolerable. I put on my hat, got into my carriage and returned to my castle.

THE DUCHESS

My poor husband! These people have simply no idea of the right way to behave to a Duke. Soon he's travelling South to our house in London, and he did so want to be able to tell the dear Queen that he had raised a whole new regiment of Highlanders to fight in her army.

And after all we have done for the people. How can they be so ungrateful?

nd so our story has come to an end. For a short time, you have been with us – the men, women and children of the Clearances.

You have had a chance to see what it was like for us during this time. Can you imagine what it felt like living on cold oatmeal and water, not just for one day but every day, and being turned out of your home with nowhere to go?

These things happened in Scotland a long time ago. Life in the Highlands and Islands is very different now. But the wide glens and the green hillsides, where the children of the Clearances once lived, are still empty. Except, of course, for the sound of sheep . . .

NOTE: The stories in this book are based on actual accounts of events, related in *The History of the Highland Clearances* by Alexander Mackenzie, first published in 1883.